A Christmas Carol Book

Illustrated by Heide Mayr-Pletschen

MERRY THOUGHTS, INC. BEDFORD HILLS, N.Y. 10507

1 O Come, O Come, Emmanuel

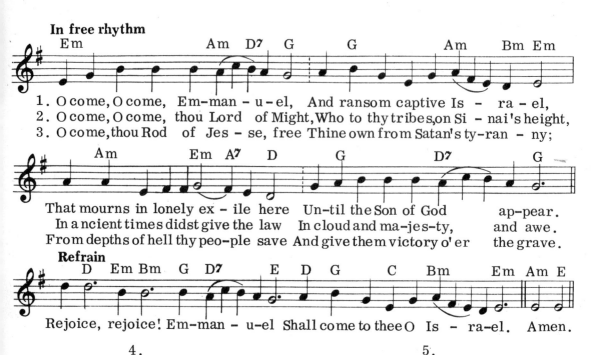

In free rhythm

1. O come, O come, Em-man - u-el, And ransom captive Is - ra - el,
2. O come, O come, thou Lord of Might, Who to thy tribes, on Si - nai's height,
3. O come, thou Rod of Jes - se, free Thine own from Satan's ty-ran - ny;

That mourns in lonely ex - ile here   Un-til the Son of God   ap-pear.
In ancient times didst give the law   In cloud and ma-jes-ty,   and awe.
From depths of hell thy peo-ple save And give them victory o'er   the grave.

Refrain

Rejoice, rejoice! Em-man - u-el Shall come to thee O Is - ra-el.   Amen.

4.

O come, thou Dayspring, come and cheer
Our spirits by thine advent here;
Disperse the gloomy clouds of night,
And death's dark shadows put to flight.
   Rejoice, rejoice! Emmanuel
   Shall come to thee, O Israel.

5.

O come, thou Key of David, come,
And open wide our heavenly home;
Make safe the way that leads on high,
And close the path to misery.
   Rejoice, rejoice! Emmanuel
   Shall come to thee, O Israel.

2 All My Heart This Night Rejoices

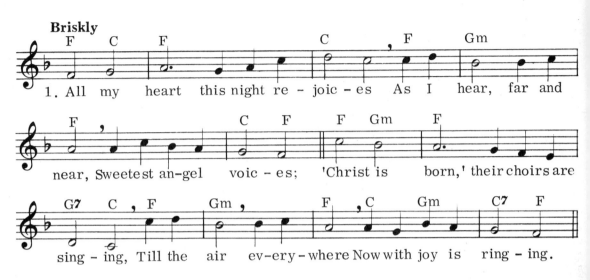

Briskly

1. All my heart this night re - joic - es As I hear, far and near, Sweetest an-gel voic - es; 'Christ is born,' their choirs are sing - ing, Till the air ev-ery-where Now with joy is ring - ing.

2.

Hark! a voice from yonder manger,
   Soft and sweet, doth entreat,
'Flee from woe and danger;
Brethren, come; from all that grieves you
   You are freed; all you need
I will surely give you.'

3.

Come then, let us hasten yonder;
   Here let all, great and small,
Kneel in awe and wonder,
Love him who with love is yearning;
   Hail the star that from far
Bright with hope is burning.

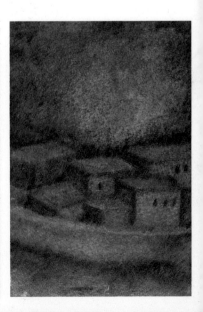

3 The Happy Christmas Comes Once More

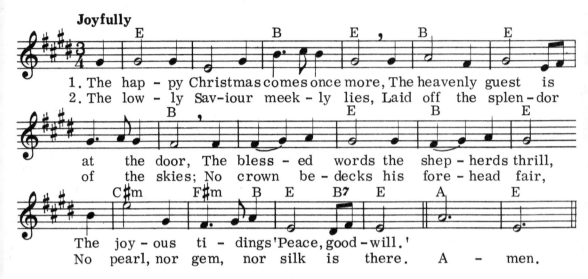

Joyfully

1. The hap - py Christmas comes once more, The heavenly guest is
2. The low - ly Sav-iour meek - ly lies, Laid off the splen - dor

at the door, The bless - ed words the shep - herds thrill,
of the skies; No crown be - decks his fore - head fair,

The joy - ous ti - dings 'Peace, good - will.'
No pearl, nor gem, nor silk is there. A - men.

3. O wake, our hearts, in gladness sing,
   And keep our Christmas with our King,
   Till living song, from loving souls,
   Like sound of mighty water rolls.

4. Come, Jesus, glorious heavenly guest,
   Keep thine own Christmas in our breast,
   Then David's harpstrings, hushed so long,
   Shall swell our jubilee of song. Amen.

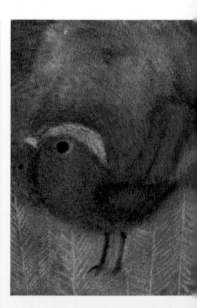

4 Silent Night! Holy Night!

Tenderly

1. Si - lent night, ho - ly night, All is calm, all is bright

Round yon Vir - gin Mother and Child. Ho - ly In - fant, so tender and mild,

Sleep in heav - en - ly peace,—— Sleep in heav - en - ly peace.

2. Silent night, holy night,
   Shepherds quake at the sight;
   Glories stream from heaven afar,
   Heavenly hosts sing, Alleluia,
   Christ, the Saviour, is born!

3. Silent night, holy night,
   Son of God, love's pure light
   Radiant beams from thy holy face,
   With the dawn of redeeming grace,
   Jesus, Lord, at thy birth.

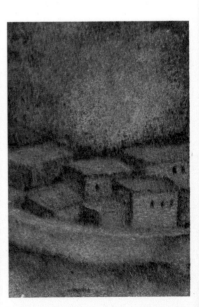

5 Thy Little Ones

Simply

1. Thy lit - tle ones, dear Lord, are we, And
2. With songs we has - ten thee to greet, And

come thy low - ly bed to see; En - light - en ev - ery
kiss the dust be - fore thy feet; O bless - ed hour, O

soul and mind, That we the way to thee may find.
sweetest night, That gave thee birth, our soul's de - light. A - men.

3.
O draw us wholly to thee, Lord.
Do thou to us thy grace accord,
True faith and love to us impart,
That we may hold thee in our heart.

4.
Until at last we too proclaim
With all thy saints, thy glorious Name;
In paradise our songs renew,
And praise thee as the angels do. Amen.

6 It Came upon the Midnight Clear

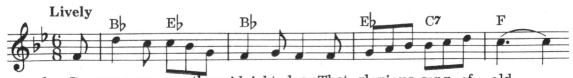

Lively

1. It came up-on the midnight clear, That glorious song of old,
2. Still thro' the clo-ven skies they come, With peaceful wings un-furled;
3. For lo! the days are has-t'ning on, By prophets seen of old,

From an-gels bend-ing near the earth, To touch their harps of gold:
And still their heav'nly mu - sic floats O'er all the wear - y world:
When with the ev - er-cir-cling years Shall come the time fore - told,

"Peace on the earth, good will to men From heav'ns all gracious King,"
A - bove its sad and low-ly plains They bend on hov-'ring wing,
When the new heav'n and earth shall own The Prince of Peace their King,

The world in sol-emn stillness lay To hear the an - gels sing.
And ev - er o'er its Babel sounds The bless-ed an - gels sing.
And the whole world send back the song Which now the an - gels sing.

7 Joy to the World

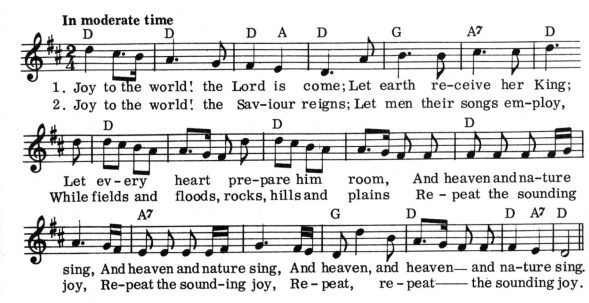

In moderate time

1. Joy to the world! the Lord is come; Let earth re-ceive her King;
2. Joy to the world! the Sav-iour reigns; Let men their songs em-ploy,

Let ev-ery heart pre-pare him room, And heaven and na-ture
While fields and floods, rocks, hills and plains Re - peat the sounding

sing, And heaven and nature sing, And heaven, and heaven— and na-ture sing.
joy, Re-peat the sound-ing joy, Re - peat, re - peat—— the sounding joy.

3.

No more let sins and sorrows grow,
Nor thorns infest the ground;
He comes to make his blessings flow
Far as the curse is found.

4.

He rules the world with truth and grace,
And makes the nations prove
The glories of his righteousness,
And wonders of his love.

8 O Little Town of Bethlehem

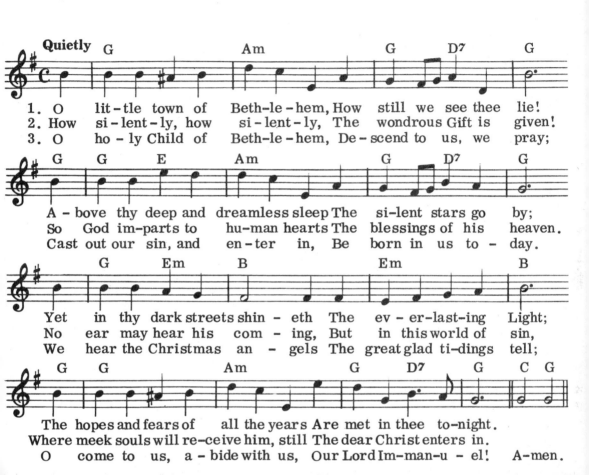

Quietly

| G | Am | G | D7 | G |

1. O lit-tle town of Beth-le-hem, How still we see thee lie!
2. How si-lent-ly, how si-lent-ly, The wondrous Gift is given!
3. O ho-ly Child of Beth-le-hem, De-scend to us, we pray;

| G | G | E | Am | G | D7 | G |

A - bove thy deep and dreamless sleep The si-lent stars go by;
So God im-parts to hu-man hearts The blessings of his heaven.
Cast out our sin, and en-ter in, Be born in us to - day.

| G | Em | B | Em | B |

Yet in thy dark streets shin - eth The ev - er-last-ing Light;
No ear may hear his com - ing, But in this world of sin,
We hear the Christmas an - gels The great glad ti-dings tell;

| G | G | Am | G | D7 | G | C | G |

The hopes and fears of all the years Are met in thee to-night.
Where meek souls will re-ceive him, still The dear Christ enters in.
O come to us, a - bide with us, Our Lord Im-man-u - el! A-men.

9 While Shepherds Watched Their Flocks

In moderate time

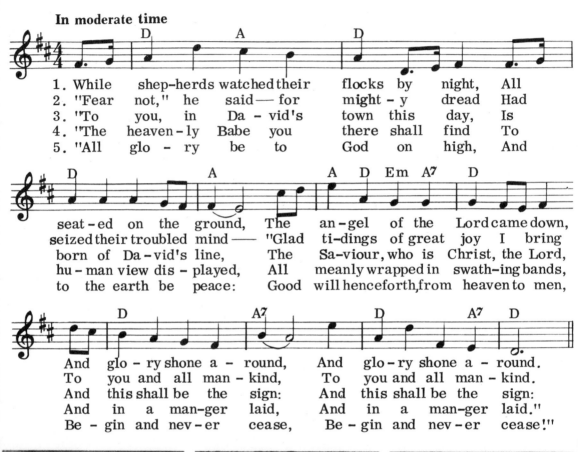

1. While shep-herds watched their flocks by night, All
2. "Fear not," he said— for might-y dread Had
3. "To you, in Da-vid's town this day, Is
4. "The heaven-ly Babe you there shall find To
5. "All glo-ry be to God on high, And

seat-ed on the ground, The an-gel of the Lord came down,
seized their troubled mind—— "Glad ti-dings of great joy I bring
born of Da-vid's line, The Sa-viour, who is Christ, the Lord,
hu-man view dis-played, All meanly wrapped in swath-ing bands,
to the earth be peace: Good will henceforth, from heaven to men,

And glo-ry shone a-round, And glo-ry shone a-round.
To you and all man-kind, To you and all man-kind.
And this shall be the sign: And this shall be the sign:
And in a man-ger laid, And in a man-ger laid."
Be-gin and nev-er cease, Be-gin and nev-er cease!"

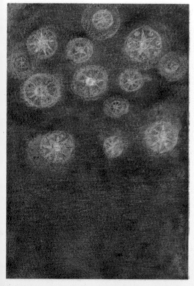

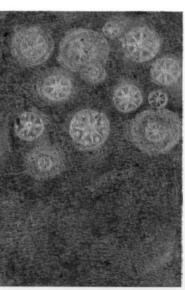

10 From Heaven Above

Flowing

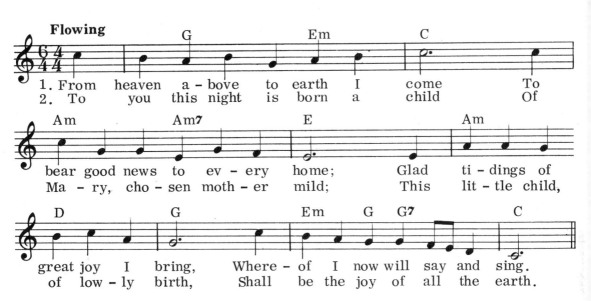

G   Em   C

1. From heaven a – bove to earth I come To
2. To you this night is born a child Of

Am   Am7   E   Am

bear good news to ev – ery home;   Glad ti – dings of
Ma – ry, cho – sen moth – er mild;   This lit – tle child,

D   G   Em G G7   C

great joy I bring, Where – of I now will say and sing.
of low – ly birth, Shall be the joy of all the earth.

3. Were earth a thousand times as fair,
Beset with gold and jewels rare,
She yet were far too poor to be
A narrow cradle, Lord, to thee.

4. Ah, dearest Jesus, Holy Child,
Make thee a bed, soft undefiled,
Within my heart, that it may be
A quiet chamber kept for thee.

5. 'Glory to God in highest heaven,
Who unto man his Son hath given,'
While angels sing with pious mirth
A glad new year to all the earth.

11   Good Christian Men Rejoice

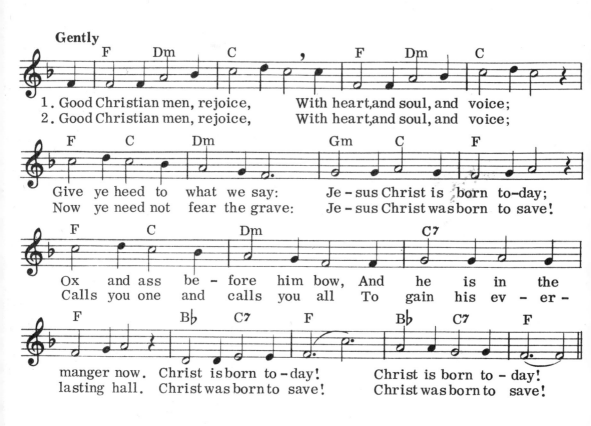

Gently

F Dm C , F Dm C

1. Good Christian men, rejoice,   With heart, and soul, and voice;
2. Good Christian men, rejoice,   With heart, and soul, and voice;

F C Dm Gm C F

Give ye heed to what we say: Je - sus Christ is born to-day;
Now ye need not fear the grave: Je - sus Christ was born to save!

F C Dm C7

Ox and ass be - fore him bow, And he is in the
Calls you one and calls you all To gain his ev - er -

F Bb C7 F Bb C7 F

manger now. Christ is born to - day!   Christ is born to - day!
lasting hall. Christ was born to save!   Christ was born to save!

12   I am so Glad Each Christmas Eve

With movement

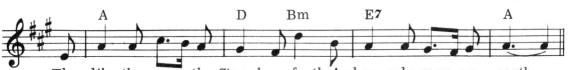

1. I am so glad each Christmas Eve, The night of Je-sus' birth!
2. The lit-tle Child in Beth-le-hem, He was a King in-deed!
3. He dwells a-gain in heaven's realm, The Son of God to-day;
4. I am so glad on Christmas Eve! His praises then I sing;
5. When mother trims the Christmas tree Which fills the room with light,

Then like the sun the Star shone forth, And an-gels sang on earth.
For he came down from heaven above To help a world in need.
And still he loves his lit-tle ones And hears them when they pray.
He o-pens then for ev-ery child The pal-ace of the King.
She tells me of the wondrous Star That made the dark world bright.

6. She says the Star is shining still,
   And never will grow dim;
   And if it shines upon my way,
   It leads me up to him.

7. And so I love each Christmas Eve
   And I love Jesus, too;
   And that he loves me every day
   I know so well is true.

Jeg er saa glad hver julekveld;
ti da blev Jesus født,
da lyste stjernen som en sol,
og engle sang saa sødt.

13 O Come, All Ye Faithful

In moderate time

1. O come, all ye faith - ful, joy - ful and tri - um-phant, O come ye, O come ye to Beth - le - hem!
2. Sing, choirs of an - gels, sing in ex - ul - ta - tion, O sing, all ye cit-i-zens of heaven a - bove!

Come and be - hold him, born the King of an - gels:
Glo - ry to God, all glo - ry in the high - est:

Refrain

O come, let us a - dore him, O come, let us a - dore him, O come, let us a - dore him, Christ, the Lord!

14   What Child is This?

In moderate time

1. What child is this, who, laid to rest, On Ma-ry's lap is sleep-ing?
2. So bring him incense, gold, and myrrh, Come, peasant, king, to own him;

Whom angels greet with anthems sweet, While shepherds watch are keeping?
The King of kings sal-va-tion brings, Let lov-ing hearts enthrone him.

Refrain

This,   this   is Christ the King, Whom shepherds guard and an-gels sing;

Haste,   haste to   bring him laud, The Babe, the son   of   Ma-ry.

15 We Three Kings of Orient Are

Lively

1. We three kings of O-ri-ent are, Bear-ing gifts we traverse a-far
2. Born a King on Bethlehem's plain, Gold I bring to crown Him a-gain,
3. Frank-in-cense to of-fer have I, In-cense owns a De-i-ty nigh;
4. Myrrh is mine; its bit-ter per-fume Breathes a life of gath-er-ing gloom:
5. Glo-rious now be-hold Him a-rise, King and God and Sac-ri-fice;

Field and foun-tain, moor and moun-tain, Fol-low-ing yon-der star.
King for-ev-er, ceas-ing nev-er O-ver us all to reign.
Prayer and prais-ing, all men rais-ing, Wor ship Him, God on high.
Sor-r'wing, sigh-ing, bleed-ing, dy-ing, Sealed in the stone-cold tomb.
Al-le-lu-ia, al-le-lu-ia! Earth to heav'n re-plies.

O—— star of won-der, star of night, Star with roy-al beau-ty bright,

West-ward lead-ing, still pro-ceed-ing, Guide us to thy per-fect light.

16 O Come, Little Children

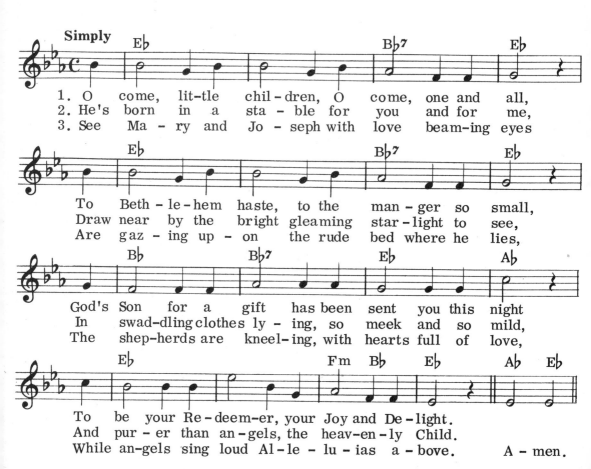

Simply

1. O come, lit-tle chil-dren, O come, one and all,
2. He's born in a sta-ble for you and for me,
3. See Ma-ry and Jo-seph with love beam-ing eyes

To Beth-le-hem haste, to the man-ger so small,
Draw near by the bright gleaming star-light to see,
Are gaz-ing up-on the rude bed where he lies,

God's Son for a gift has been sent you this night
In swad-dling clothes ly-ing, so meek and so mild,
The shep-herds are kneel-ing, with hearts full of love,

To be your Re-deem-er, your Joy and De-light.
And pur-er than an-gels, the heav-en-ly Child.
While an-gels sing loud Al-le-lu-ias a-bove. A-men.

17　The First Noel

With spirit

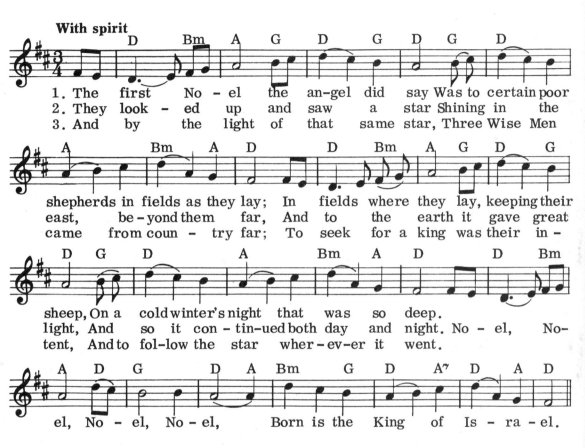

1. The first No - el the an - gel did say Was to certain poor
2. They look - ed up and saw a star Shining in the
3. And by the light of that same star, Three Wise Men

shepherds in fields as they lay; In fields where they lay, keeping their
east, be - yond them far, And to the earth it gave great
came from coun - try far; To seek for a king was their in -

sheep, On a cold winter's night that was so deep.
light, And so it con - tin - ued both day and night. No - el, No -
tent, And to fol - low the star wher - ev - er it went.

el, No - el, No - el, Born is the King of Is - ra - el.

18 God Rest Ye Merry, Gentlemen

Quite fast and stately

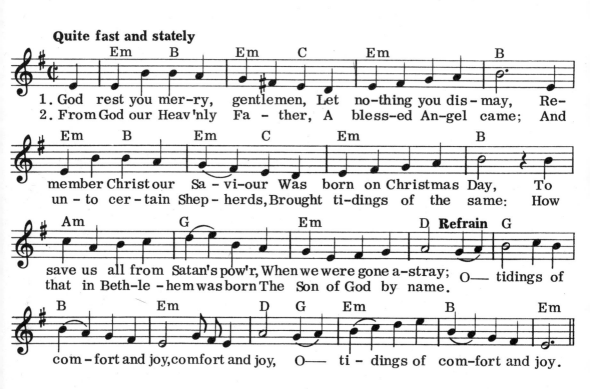

1. God rest you mer-ry, gentlemen, Let no-thing you dis-may, Re-
2. From God our Heav'nly Fa - ther, A bless-ed An-gel came; And

member Christ our Sa - vi-our Was born on Christmas Day, To
un - to cer-tain Shep - herds, Brought ti-dings of the same: How

save us all from Satan's pow'r, When we were gone a-stray; O— tidings of
that in Beth-le - hem was born The Son of God by name.

com - fort and joy, comfort and joy, O— ti - dings of com-fort and joy.

19 Angels We Have Heard on High

Smoothly

1. An-gels we have heard on high, Sweet-ly sing-ing o'er the plains;
2. Come to Beth-le - hem, and see Him whose birth the an - gels sing;
3. Les an-ges dans nos cam-pagnes ont enton-né l'hym-ne des cieux,

And the mountains in re-ply Ech - o - ing their joy - ous strains.
Come a-dore on bend - ed knee, Christ, the Lord, our new-born King.
et l'é - cho de nos mon-tagnes re - dit ce chant mé - lo - di-eux:

Refrain

Glo - - - - ri - a

in ex - cel - sis De - o, Glo - - -

- - ri - a in ex-cel - sis De - o.

20 Angels from the Realms of Glory

Dignified

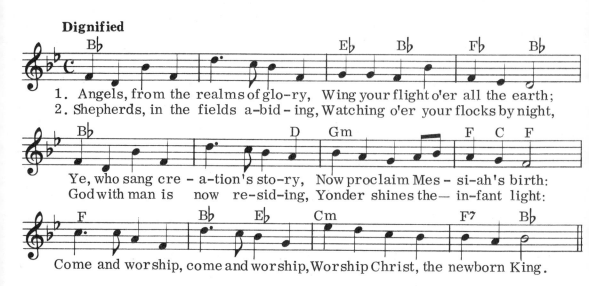

1. Angels, from the realms of glo-ry, Wing your flight o'er all the earth;
2. Shepherds, in the fields a-bid-ing, Watching o'er your flocks by night,

Ye, who sang cre - a-tion's sto-ry, Now proclaim Mes - si-ah's birth:
God with man is now re-sid-ing, Yonder shines the— in-fant light:

Come and wor ship, come and wor ship, Worship Christ, the newborn King.

3. Sages, leave your contemplations,
   Brighter visions beam afar;
   See the great Desire of nations,
   Ye have seen his natal star:

4. All creation, join in praising
   God, the Father, Spirit, Son,
   Evermore your voices raising
   To the eternal Three in One:

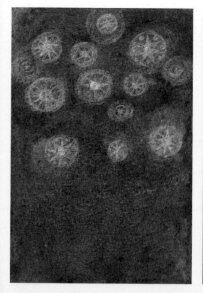

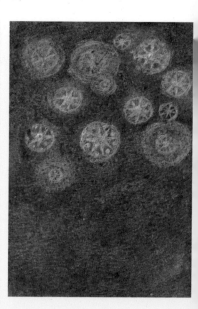

21 Hark, the Herald Angels Sing

In moderat time

Hark, the her-ald an-gels sing, 'Glo-ry to the newborn King;

Peace on earth, and mer-cy mild, God and sin-ners rec-on-ciled!'

Joy-ful, all ye nations, rise, Join the tri-umph of the skies,

With the angelic host pro-claim, 'Christ is— born in Beth-le-hem.

Hark, the her-ald an-gels sing, 'Glo-ry— to the newborn King!'

22 Lo, How a Rose E'er Blooming

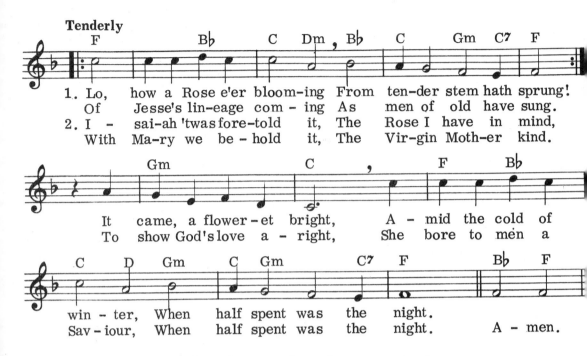

Tenderly

F — Bb — C — Dm , Bb — C — Gm — C7 — F

1. Lo, how a Rose e'er bloom-ing From ten-der stem hath sprung!
Of Jesse's lin-eage com - ing As men of old have sung.
2. I - sai-ah 'twas fore-told it, The Rose I have in mind,
With Ma-ry we be - hold it, The Vir-gin Moth-er kind.

Gm — C , F — Bb

It came, a flower - et bright, A - mid the cold of
To show God's love a - right, She bore to men a

C D Gm C Gm C7 F Bb F

win - ter, When half spent was the night.
Sav - iour, When half spent was the night. A - men.

3. This Flower, whose fragrance tender
With sweetness fills the air,
Dispels with glorious splendor
The darkness everywhere.
True Man, yet very God,
From sin and death he saves us
And lightens every load.

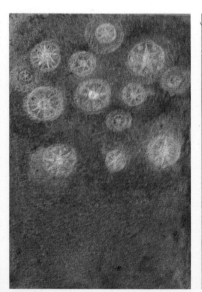

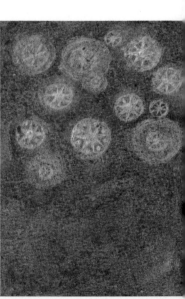

23 Deck the Hall

Lively

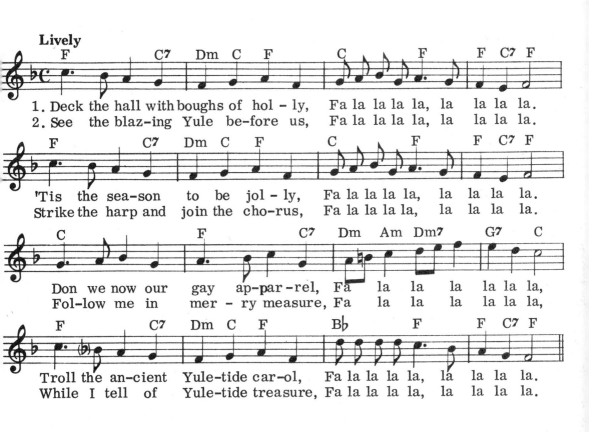

1. Deck the hall with boughs of hol - ly, Fa la la la la, la la la la.
2. See the blaz-ing Yule be-fore us, Fa la la la la, la la la la.

'Tis the sea-son to be jol - ly, Fa la la la la, la la la la.
Strike the harp and join the cho-rus, Fa la la la la, la la la la.

Don we now our gay ap-par -rel, Fa la la la la la la,
Fol-low me in mer - ry measure, Fa la la la la la la,

Troll the an-cient Yule-tide car-ol, Fa la la la la, la la la la.
While I tell of Yule-tide treasure, Fa la la la la, la la la la.

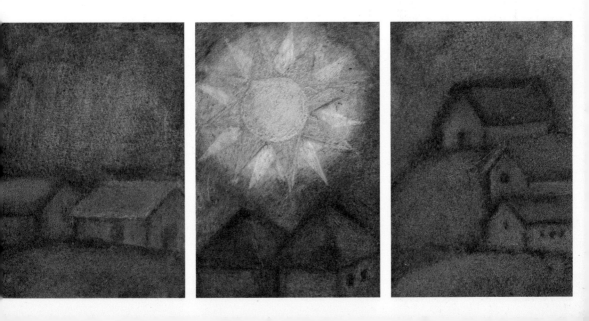

24　O Christmas Tree

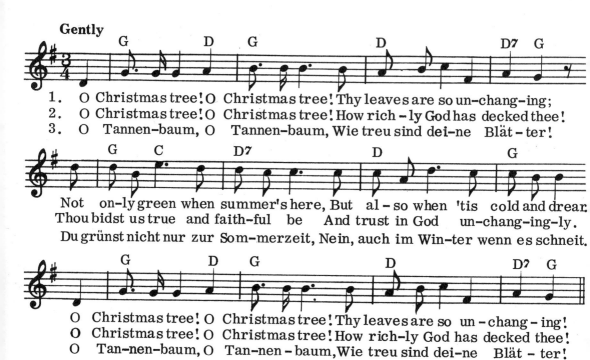

Gently

1. O Christmas tree! O Christmas tree! Thy leaves are so un-chang-ing;
2. O Christmas tree! O Christmas tree! How rich-ly God has decked thee!
3. O Tannen-baum, O Tannen-baum, Wie treu sind dei-ne Blät-ter!

Not on-ly green when summer's here, But al-so when 'tis cold and drear.
Thou bidst us true and faith-ful be And trust in God un-chang-ing-ly.
Du grünst nicht nur zur Som-merzeit, Nein, auch im Win-ter wenn es schneit.

O Christmas tree! O Christmas tree! Thy leaves are so un-chang-ing!
O Christmas tree! O Christmas tree! How rich-ly God has decked thee!
O Tan-nen-baum, O Tan-nen-baum, Wie treu sind dei-ne Blät-ter!

25   I Heard the Bells on Christmas Day

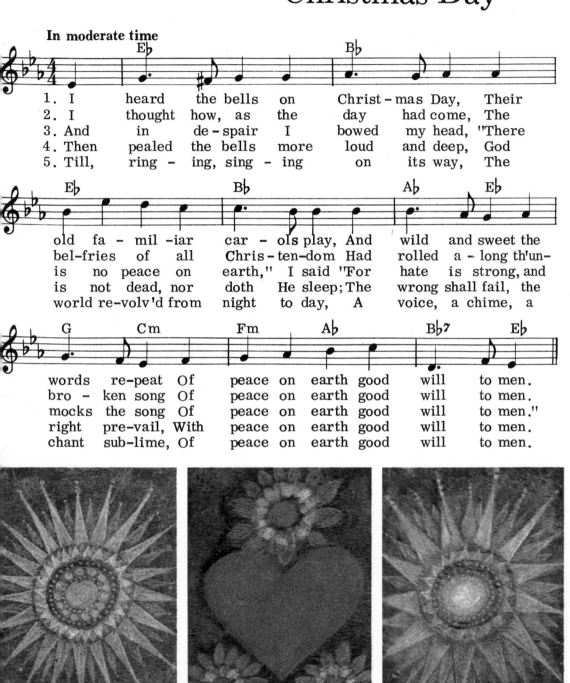

In moderate time

1. I heard the bells on Christ-mas Day, Their
2. I thought how, as the day had come, The
3. And in de-spair I bowed my head, "There
4. Then pealed the bells more loud and deep, God
5. Till, ring-ing, sing-ing on its way, The

old fa-mil-iar car-ols play, And wild and sweet the
bel-fries of all Chris-ten-dom Had rolled a-long th'un-
is no peace on earth," I said "For hate is strong, and
is not dead, nor doth He sleep; The wrong shall fail, the
world re-volv'd from night to day, A voice, a chime, a

words re-peat Of peace on earth good will to men.
bro-ken song Of peace on earth good will to men.
mocks the song Of peace on earth good will to men."
right pre-vail, With peace on earth good will to men.
chant sub-lime, Of peace on earth good will to men.

26 Away in a Manger

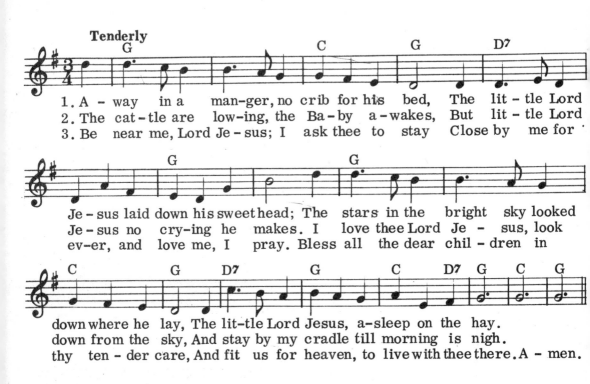

Tenderly

1. A - way in a man-ger, no crib for his bed, The lit - tle Lord
2. The cat - tle are low - ing, the Ba - by a - wakes, But lit - tle Lord
3. Be near me, Lord Je - sus; I ask thee to stay Close by me for

Je - sus laid down his sweet head; The stars in the bright sky looked
Je - sus no cry-ing he makes. I love thee Lord Je - sus, look
ev - er, and love me, I pray. Bless all the dear chil - dren in

down where he lay, The lit-tle Lord Jesus, a-sleep on the hay.
down from the sky, And stay by my cradle till morning is nigh.
thy ten - der care, And fit us for heaven, to live with thee there. A - men.

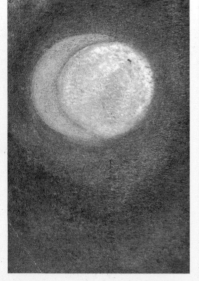

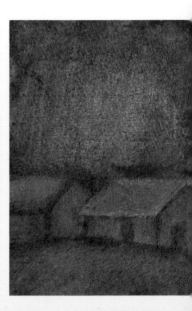